The Owl and the Pussy-cat
and other poems

Compiled by Tig Thomas

Miles Kelly

First published in 2010 by Miles Kelly Publishing Ltd
Harding's Barn, Bardfield End Green, Thaxted, Essex, CM6 3PX, UK

This edition printed in 2011

2 4 6 8 10 9 7 5 3

Editorial Director Belinda Gallagher

Art Director Jo Cowan

Assistant Editor Claire Philip

Designer Joe Jones

Junior Designer Kayleigh Allen

Production Manager Elizabeth Collins

Reprographics Stephan Davis, Ian Paulyn

ISBN 978-1-84810-365-8

Printed in China

British Library Cataloguing-in-Publication Data
A catalogue record for this book is available from the British Library

ACKNOWLEDGEMENTS

The publishers would like to thank Kirsten Wilson for
the illustrations she contributed to this book.

All other artwork from the Miles Kelly Artwork Bank

The publishers would like to thank mcswin/iStockphoto.com
for the use of their photograph on page 17

Made with paper from a sustainable forest

www.mileskelly.net
info@mileskelly.net

www.factsforprojects.com

Self-publish your
children's book

buddingpress.co.uk

Contents

The Owl and the Pussy-cat

The Owl and the Pussy-cat went to sea
In a beautiful pea-green boat,
They took some honey, and plenty of money,
Wrapped up in a five-pound note.
The Owl looked up to the stars above,
And sang to a small guitar,
"Oh, lovely Pussy, oh, Pussy, my love,
What a beautiful Pussy you are,
You are,
You are!
What a beautiful Pussy you are!"

Pussy said to the Owl,
   "You elegant fowl,
How charmingly sweet you sing!
Oh, let us be married; too long we
   have tarried:
But what shall we do for a ring?"
They sailed away for a year and a day,
To the land where the bong-tree grows;
And there in the wood a Piggy-wig stood,
With a ring at the end of his nose,
His nose,
His nose,
With a ring at the end of his nose.

"Dear Pig, are you willing to sell for one shilling
Your ring?" Said the Piggy, "I will."
So they took it away and were married next day
By the Turkey who lives on the hill.
They dined on mince and slices of quince,
Which they ate with a runcible spoon;
And hand in hand, on the edge of the sand,
They danced by the light of the moon,
The moon,
The moon,
They danced by the light of the moon.

Edward Lear

Alas! Alas!

Alas! Alas!
For Miss McKay!
Her knives and forks
Have run away.

And when the cups
And spoons are going,
She's sure there is
No way of knowing.

Anonymous

There was an Old Lady

There was an old lady who swallowed a fly
I don't know why she swallowed a fly – perhaps she'll die!

There was an old lady who swallowed a spider,
That wriggled and wiggled and tickled inside her,

She swallowed the spider to catch the fly;
I don't know why she swallowed a fly – perhaps she'll die!

There was an old lady who swallowed a bird;
How absurd to swallow a bird.
She swallowed the bird to catch the spider,
She swallowed the spider to catch the fly;
I don't know why she swallowed a fly – perhaps she'll die!

There was an old lady who swallowed a cat;
Fancy that to swallow a cat!
She swallowed the cat to catch the bird,
She swallowed the bird to catch the spider,
She swallowed the spider to catch the fly;
I don't know why she swallowed a fly – perhaps she'll die!

There was an old lady that swallowed a dog;
What a hog, to swallow a dog;
She swallowed the dog to catch the cat,
She swallowed the cat to catch the bird,
She swallowed the bird to catch the spider,
She swallowed the spider to catch the fly;
I don't know why she swallowed a fly – perhaps she'll die!

There was an old lady who swallowed a cow,
I don't know how she swallowed a cow;
She swallowed the cow to catch the dog,
She swallowed the dog to catch the cat,
She swallowed the cat to catch the bird,
She swallowed the bird to catch the spider,
She swallowed the spider to catch the fly;
I don't know why she swallowed a fly – perhaps she'll die!

There was an old lady who swallowed a horse,
She's dead, of course!

Anonymous

An Accident

As I was going out one day
My head fell off and rolled away,
But when I saw that it was gone,
I picked it up and put it on.

And when I got into the street
A fellow cried "Look at your feet!"
I looked at them and sadly said
"I've left them both asleep in bed!"

Anonymous

The Man of Hong Kong

There was an Old Man of Hong Kong,
Who never did anything wrong;
He lay on his back, with his head in a sack,
That innocuous old man of Hong Kong.

Edward Lear

Innocuous
harmless

Somewhere Town

Which is the way to Somewhere Town?
Oh, up in the morning early.
Over the tiles and the chimney pots,
That is the way quite clearly.

And which is the door to Somewhere Town?
Oh, up in the morning early.
The round red sun is the door to go through,
That is the way quite clearly.

Kate Greenaway

Elf Man

I met a little elf man, once,
    Down where the lilies blow.
I asked him why he was so small,
    And why he didn't grow.

He slightly frowned, and with his eye
    He looked me through and through.
"I'm quite as big for me," said he,
    "As you are big for you."

Anonymous

The Owl

When cats run home
   and light is come,
And dew is cold upon
   the ground,
And the far-off
   stream is dumb,
And the whirring
   sail goes round;
And the whirring sail goes round;
Alone and warming his five wits,
The white owl in the belfry sits.

When merry milkmaids click the latch,
And rarely smells the new-mown hay,
And the cock hath sung beneath the thatch
Twice or thrice his roundelay,
Twice or thrice his roundelay;
Alone and warming his five wits,
The white owl in the belfry sits.

Alfred, Lord Tennyson

Belfry bell tower
Roundelay a type of
song that repeats itself

I Asked the Little Boy who Cannot See

I asked the little boy who cannot see,
"And what is colour like?"
"Why, green," said he,
"Is like the rustle when the wind blows through
The forest; running water, that is blue;
And red is like a trumpet sound; and pink
Is like the smell of roses; and I think
That purple must be like a thunderstorm;
And yellow is like something soft and warm;
And white is a pleasant stillness when you lie
And dream."

Anonymous

The Elf and the Dormouse

Under a toadstool crept a wee Elf,
Out of the rain to shelter himself.

Under the toadstool, sound asleep,
Sat a big Dormouse all in a heap.

Trembled the wee Elf, frightened and yet
Fearing to fly away lest he get wet.

To the next shelter – maybe a mile!
Sudden the wee Elf smiled a wee smile.

Tugged till the toadstool toppled in two.
Holding it over him, gaily he flew.

Soon he was safe home, dry as could be.
Soon woke the Dormouse – "Good gracious me!"

"Where is my toadstool?" loud he lamented.
– And that's how umbrellas first were invented.

Oliver Herford

Up and Down

Up and down, up and down,
I will lead them up and down:
I am fear'd in field and town:
Goblin, lead them up and down.

William Shakespeare

These two songs are sung by Puck, a fairy created by Shakespeare, who likes to play tricks on people.

I'll Follow You

I'll follow you, I'll lead you about a round,
Through bog, through bush, through brake, through brier:
Sometime a horse I'll be, sometime a hound,
A hog, a headless bear, sometime a fire;
And neigh, and bark, and grunt, and roar, and burn,
Like horse, hound, hog, bear, fire, at every turn.

William Shakespeare

Brake a small clump of trees
Brier a bramble bush

The Peacock has a Score of Eyes

The peacock has a score of eyes,
With which he cannot see;
The cod-fish has a silent sound,
However that may be;

No dandelions tell the time,
Although they turn to clocks;
Cat's-cradle does not hold the cat,
Nor foxglove fit the fox.

Christina Rossetti

From Fairy King

"The breeze is on the Bluebells,
  The wind is on the leaf;
Stay out! Stay out! My little lad,
  And chase the wind with me.
If you will give yourself to me,
  Within the fairy ring,
    At deep midnight,
    When stars are bright,
You'll hear the Bluebells ring –

D!
DI! DIN!
DING!

On slender stems they swing.

"The rustling wind, the whistling wind,
  We'll chase him to and fro,
We'll chase him up, we'll chase him down
  To where the King-cups grow;
And where old Jack-o'-Lantern waits
  To light us on our way,
And far behind,
  Upon the wind,
  The Bluebells seem to play –

D!
DI! DIN!
DING!

Lest we should go astray.

Juliana Horatia Ewing

Meg Merrilies

Old Meg she was a Gipsy,
　　And liv'd upon the Moors:
Her bed it was the brown heath turf,
　　And her house was out of doors.
Her apples were swart blackberries,
　　Her currants pods o' broom;
Her wine was dew of the wild white rose,
　　Her book a churchyard tomb.
Her Brothers were the craggy hills,
　　Her Sisters larchen trees –
Alone with her great family
　　She liv'd as she did please.
No breakfast had she many a morn,
　　No dinner many a noon,
And 'stead of supper she would stare
　　Full hard against the Moon.

But every morn of woodbine fresh
    She made her garlanding,
And every night the dark glen Yew
    She wove, and she would sing.
And with her fingers old and brown
    She plaited Mats o' Rushes,
And gave them to the Cottagers
    She met among the Bushes.
Old Meg was brave as Margaret Queen
    And tall as Amazon:
An old red blanket cloak she wore;
    A chip hat had she on.
God rest her aged bones somewhere –
    She died full long agone!

John Keats

Garlanding a flowery ring or wreath
Woodbine honeysuckle

A Tale of Wonders

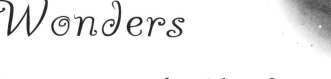

I saw a peacock with a fiery tail
I saw a blazing comet drop down hail
I saw a cloud with ivy circled round
I saw a sturdy oak creep on the ground
I saw a pismire swallow up a whale
I saw a raging sea brim full of ale
I saw a Venice glass sixteen foot deep
I saw a well full of men's tears that weep
I saw their eyes all in a flame of fire
I saw a house as big as the moon and higher
I saw the sun even in the midst of night
I saw the man who saw this wondrous sight

Anonymous

Pismire ant

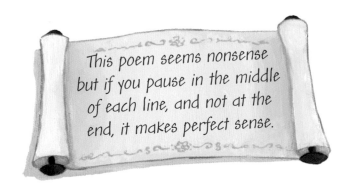

This poem seems nonsense but if you pause in the middle of each line, and not at the end, it makes perfect sense.

The Fairies' Dance

Dare you haunt our hallow'd green?
None but fairies here are seen.
Down and sleep.
Wake and weep,
Pinch him black, and pinch him blue,
That seeks to steal a lover true!

Hallow'd holy

When you come to hear us sing,
Or to tread our fairy ring,
Pinch him black, and pinch him blue!
O thus our nails shall handle you!

John Lyly

The Song of a Giant

Fee, Fie, Foh, Fum!

I smell the blood of an
Englishman –
Be he alive or be he dead,
I'll grind his bones to
make my bread.

Anonymous

The Roses

You love the roses – so do I. I wish
The sky would rain down roses, as they rain
From off the shaken bush. Why will it not?
Then all the valley would be pink and white
And soft to tread on. They would fall as light
As feathers, smelling sweet; and it would be
Like sleeping and like waking,
all at once!

George Eliot

Jack Frost

Jack Frost is an imaginary creature who is said to paint patterns on windowpanes with frost.

The door was shut, as doors should be,
Before you went to bed last night;
Yet Jack Frost has got in, you see,
And left your window silver white.

He must have waited till you slept;
And not a single word he spoke,
But pencilled o'er the panes and crept
Away again before you woke.

And now you cannot see the hills
Nor fields that stretch beyond the lane;
But there are fairer things than these
His fingers traced on every pane.

Rocks and castles towering high;
Hills and dales, and streams and fields;
And knights in armour riding by,
With nodding plumes and shining shields.

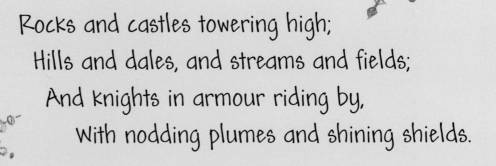

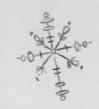

And here are little boats, and there
      Big ships with sails spread to the breeze;
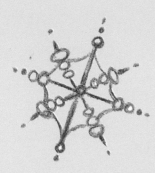And yonder, palm trees waving fair
      On islands set in silver seas,

And butterflies with gauzy wings;
    And herds of cows and flocks of sheep;
And fruit and flowers and all the things
    You see when you are sound asleep.

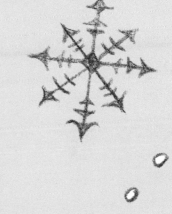

For, creeping softly underneath
    The door when all the lights are out,
Jack Frost takes every breath you breathe,
    And knows the things you think about.

He paints them on the windowpane
    In fairy lines with frozen steam;
And when you wake you see again
    The lovely things you saw in dream.

Gabriel Setoun

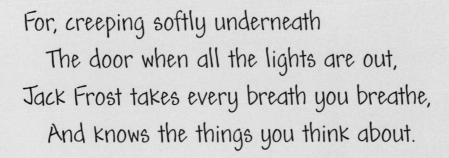

Nine Little Goblins

They all climbed up on a high board-fence,
Nine little Goblins that had no sense,
Nine little Goblins, with green-glass eyes,
And couldn't tell coppers from cold mince pies;
And they all climbed up on the
fence, and sat,
And I asked them what they
were staring at.

And the first one said, as he
scratched his head
With a queer little arm that
reached out of his ear

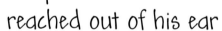

And rasped its claws in his hair so red,
"This is what this little arm is for!"
And he scratched and stared, and the
    next one said,
"How on earth do you scratch
    your head ?"

And he laughed like the
    screech of a rusty hinge,
Laughed and laughed till
    his face grew black;
And when he clicked, with a
    final twinge
Of his stifling laughter, he thumped
    his back
With a fist that grew on the end of his tail
Till the breath came back to his lips so pale.

And the third little Goblin
    leered round at me,
And there were no lids on his
    eyes at all
And he clucked one eye, and he
    says, says he,
"What is the style of your socks
    this fall?"
And he clapped his heels and I
    sighed to see
That he had hands where his feet
    should be.

Then a bald-faced Goblin, grey and grim,
Bowed his head, and I saw him slip
His eyebrows off, as I looked at him,
And paste them over his upper lip;
And then he moaned in remorseful pain,
"Would, ah, would I'd me brows again!"

And then the whole of the Goblin band
Rocked on the fence-top to and fro,
And clung, in a long row, hand in hand,
Singing the songs that they used to know,
Singing the songs that their grandsires sung
In the goo-goo days of the Goblin-tongue.

And ever they kept their green-glass eyes
Fixed on me with a stony stare,
Till my own grew glazed with a dread surmise,
And my hat whooped up on my lifted hair,
And I felt the heart in my breast snap to
As you've heard the lid of a snuff box do.

And they sang "You're asleep! There is no board-fence,
And never a Goblin with green-glass eyes!
"'Tis only a vision the mind invents
After a supper of cold mince pies,
And you're doomed to dream this way," they said,
"And you shan't wake up till you're clean plumb dead!"

James Whitcomb Riley

The Lamplighter

My tea is nearly ready and the sun has left the sky.
It's time to take the window to see Leerie going by;
For every night at teatime and before you take your seat,
With lantern and with ladder he comes posting up the street.

Now Tom would be a driver and Maria go to sea,
And my papa's a banker and as rich as he can be;
But I, when I am stronger and can choose what
    I'm to do,
O Leerie, I'll go round at night and light the
    lamps with you!

For we are very lucky, with a lamp before the door,
And Leerie stops to light it as he lights so
    many more;
And oh! before you hurry by with
    ladder and with light;
O Leerie, see a little child and nod to
    him tonight!

Robert Louis Stevenson

Street lamps used to
be lit by gas, and a
lamplighter had to
light each one.

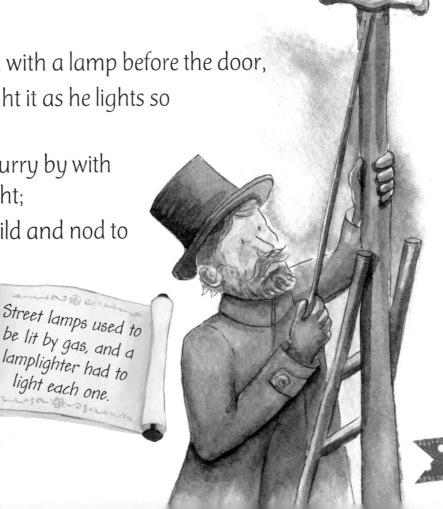

Minnie and Winnie

Minnie and Winnie
Slept in a shell.
Sleep, little ladies!
And they slept well.

Pink was the shell within,
Silver without;
Sounds of the great sea
Wandered about.

Sleep little ladies!
Wake not soon!
Echo on echo
Dies to the moon.

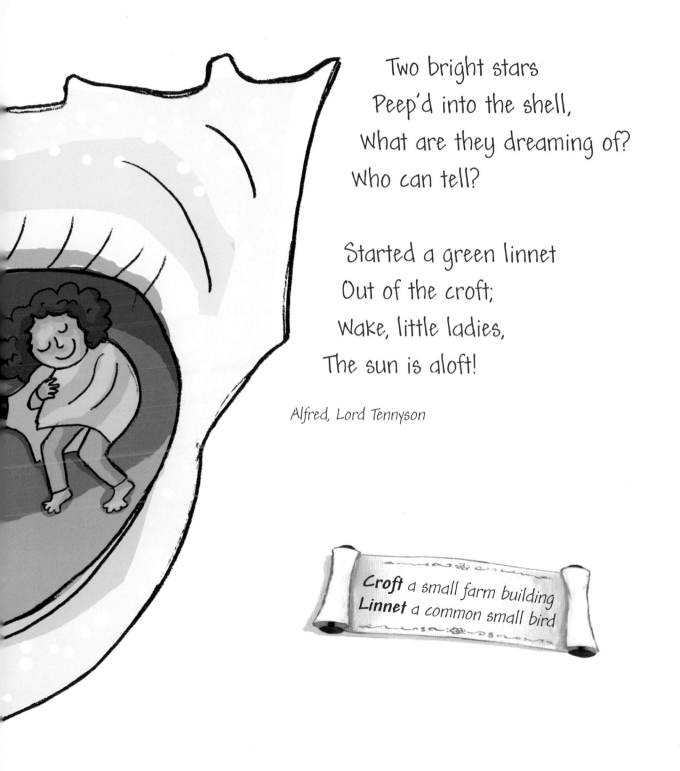

Two bright stars
　Peep'd into the shell,
　　What are they dreaming of?
　Who can tell?

　Started a green linnet
　Out of the croft;
　Wake, little ladies,
The sun is aloft!

Alfred, Lord Tennyson

Croft a small farm building
Linnet a common small bird

Index of First Lines